Word Problems
with
Instant Assessment
Grade 4

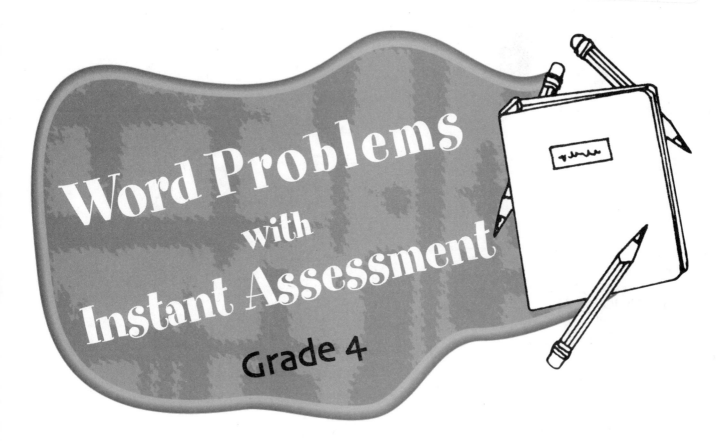

by
M.J. Owen

Carson-Dellosa Publishing Company, Inc.
Greensboro, North Carolina

Credits

Editor
Amy Gamble

Layout Design
Jon Nawrocik

Inside Illustrations
Veronica Terrill
Wayne Miller

Cover Design
Penn Dragon Design

Printed in the USA • All rights reserved.   ISBN 0-88724-930-2

Table of Contents

As an elementary school teacher, I've watched many of my students struggle with problem solving. I didn't think the problem was that my students couldn't solve basic facts; I thought it ran deeper than that. I decided that my students were struggling with word problems for two reasons: they weren't quite sure what the problem was asking and they frequently did not even know where to start.

I hope this book will be useful in teaching students how to overcome these issues. The book provides students with a step-by-step approach to solving word problems. It puts the focus on solving the problem rather than on the actual answer. The format requires the student to show his understanding of what the problem is asking, his problem-solving plan, and the meaning of his answer. This makes the problems easy to check and allows for quick identification of where students are struggling.

I found that the more kids practiced the process of arriving at the right answer, the more confident they became as problem solvers. May your students' road to problem-solving success be filled with learning and fun!

mg Owen

How to Use This Book

The problems in this book are arranged in groups of five. At the beginning of each group of five problems, step-by-step directions are given to guide students through the steps of effective problem solving (see box at right).

Directions:
1. Read the word problem.
2. Underline the facts you will need to solve the problem.
3. Circle the letter beside the number sentence you should use to solve the problem.
4. Solve the problem. Show your work in the box. Your work may include a drawing.
5. Write your answer on the line.
6. Write your answer as a complete sentence.

The directions ask the student to first read the word problem. Many students miss important details because they skip straight to the question portion of the problem.

Next, the student is asked to focus on the relevant information in the problem by underlining the important facts (see example problem below). Here, the student practices distinguishing relevant information from irrelevant and identifying key math words and phrases, such as *more*, *less*, *altogether*, *bought*, *left over*, etc.

Example Problem:

Zach <u>bought</u> a treat for <u>55¢</u> from the ice-cream truck. If Zach has <u>16¢ left over</u>, how much money did he have <u>to start with</u>?

A. 16¢ – 5¢ =

B. 55¢ + 16¢ =

C. 55¢ + 10¢ =

D. 55¢ – 16¢ =

The third step is one that students most often skip to first. In this step, the student practices translating the underlined facts into an equation that can be used to solve the problem. He must choose the correct number sentence from four choices (see example problem at left).

The next step is important in assessment. Here, the student does the actual math and the teacher is able to see the student's work in the *Show Your Work* box. The student may choose to solve the problem traditionally or draw a picture, diagram, or other symbolic representation (see examples at right).

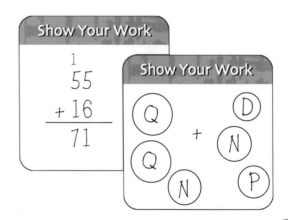

Finally, the student writes his answer on the line and writes the answer in a complete sentence (see example at right). Writing the answer in a complete sentence helps the student attach meaning to the answer and helps the teacher more easily assess the student's understanding.

Answer: _____71¢_____

Sentence: _Zach had 71¢ to start with._

At the end of each five-problem section, the teacher can easily assess each part of the problem-solving process with the *Instant Assessment Checklist*. The assessment can be as simple or as detailed as desired. A simple check can be made for each step that is effectively completed, or a system of checks, minuses, and pluses can be used to give more detail about whether the step was attempted or not and whether it was correct or not. Also, the spaces are large enough to write brief notes about the student's progress with any step.

Instant Assessment Checklist

Problem Number	Facts Underlined	Number Sentence Chosen	Work Shown	Answer Written	Sentence Completed
1	✔	✔	✔	✔	✔
2	✔ +	+ +	✔ −	✔ +	−
3	most facts found	correct choice	unrelated picture	correct but no units given	nothing written
4					
5					

The review section at the end of the book offers a five-problem section for each of the math skills covered in the book. The reviews can be used after each skill section is completed or all together at the end of the year for an overall review.

Name _____

Directions:
1. Read the word problem.
2. Underline the facts you will need to solve the problem.
3. Circle the letter beside the number sentence you should use to solve the problem.
4. Solve the problem. Show your work in the box. Your work may include a drawing.
5. Write your answer on the line.
6. Write your answer as a complete sentence.

Going to Grandma's

Add & Subtract: 3-Digit

1. Matt is traveling 327 miles to visit his grandmother. His friend Kate will travel 255 miles to visit her grandparents. How much farther will Matt travel than Kate?

   A. 327 − 255 =

   B. 355 + 227 =

   C. 372 − 372 =

   D. 327 + 255 =

   Answer: _____

   Sentence: _____

   Show Your Work

2. Cora and Sam are each visiting their grandparents for the summer. Sam will travel 76 miles by car and Cora will travel 170 miles by bus. How many miles will Cora and Sam travel in all?

   A. 170 − 170 =

   B. 170 + 76 =

   C. 76 + 76 =

   D. 170 − 76 =

   Answer: _____

   Sentence: _____

   Show Your Work

Name _____

3. Chelsea's family drives 578 miles to see her grandmother. On the way home, they stop to visit friends, which means that they drive an additional 125 miles. How many miles does Chelsea's family drive on the way home from her grandmother's house?

A. 125 + 125 =

B. 578 + 125 =

C. 578 + 578 =

D. 578 − 125 =

Answer: _____

Sentence: _____

_____

Show Your Work

4. Dawson is going to visit his grandmother over spring break. He will travel 254 miles by train, 171 miles by bus, and 12 miles by taxi to reach his destination. How many miles will Dawson travel in all to visit his grandmother?

A. 171 + 254 − 12 =

B. 254 − 171 =

C. 171 + 12 =

D. 254 + 171 + 12 =

Answer: _____

Sentence: _____

Show Your Work

Name _____

5. Grandma's house is located 221 miles from her grandson's house and 133 miles from her granddaughter's house. How much farther is Grandma's house from her grandson's house than her granddaughter's house?

A. 221 + 221 =

B. 221 + 133 =

C. 221 – 133 =

D. 133 – 133 =

Answer: _____

Sentence: _____

_____

Show Your Work

Instant Assessment Checklist

Problem Number	Facts Underlined	Number Sentence Chosen	Work Shown	Answer Written	Sentence Completed
1					
2					
3					
4					
5					

Name _____

Directions:
1. Read the word problem.
2. Underline the facts you will need to solve the problem.
3. Circle the letter beside the number sentence you should use to solve the problem.
4. Solve the problem. Show your work in the box. Your work may include a drawing.
5. Write your answer on the line.
6. Write your answer as a complete sentence.

Trip to the Mountains

Add & Subtract: 4-Digit

1. Marissa's family visited a park in the mountains this summer. They flew 1,589 miles to the park. If their flight was round-trip, how many miles did they fly in all?

   A. 1,589 – 1,589 =

   B. 1,589 + 1,589 =

   C. 1,589 + 1,000 =

   D. 1,589 – 1,000 =

   Answer: _____

   Sentence: _____

   Show Your Work

2. The family saw 2 big mountains. Hammer's Peak's elevation is 3,349 feet and Overlook Peak's elevation is 5,220 feet. How much taller is Overlook Peak than Hammer's Peak?

   A. 3,349 + 2,000 =

   B. 5,220 + 3,349 =

   C. 5,220 – 2,000 =

   D. 5,220 – 3,349 =

   Answer: _____

   Sentence: _____

   Show Your Work

Name _____

Add & Subtract: 4-Digit

3. During the 2 weeks that Marissa's family visited the park, the park service recorded 6,725 visitors. If 2,861 of the visitors were from out of the country, how many visitors were from within the country?

   A. 6,725 + 6,725 =

   B. 6,725 − 2,861 =

   C. 6,725 − 2,000 =

   D. 6,725 + 2,861 =

   Answer: _____

   Sentence: _____

   _____

Show Your Work

4. Marissa's older brothers went white-water rafting and camped out overnight. If they paddled 4,250 meters down the river the first day and 3,955 meters the second day, how many meters of river did the brothers paddle down altogether?

   A. 4,250 + 3,955 =

   B. 4,250 + 4,250 =

   C. 4,250 − 3,955 =

   D. 3,955 − 3,955 =

   Answer: _____

   Sentence: _____

Show Your Work

Name _____

5. Marissa's mother remembers visiting the same park with her family in 1967 when she was a young girl. If it is now 2004, how many years have passed since Marissa's mother last visited the park?

A. 2004 + 1967 =

B. 1967 + 4 =

C. 2004 – 1967 =

D. 1967 + 1967 =

Answer: _____

Sentence: _____

_____

Show Your Work

Instant Assessment Checklist

Problem Number	Facts Underlined	Number Sentence Chosen	Work Shown	Answer Written	Sentence Completed
1					
2					
3					
4					
5					

Name _____

Directions:
1. Read the word problem.
2. Underline the facts you will need to solve the problem.
3. Circle the letter beside the number sentence you should use to solve the problem.
4. Solve the problem. Show your work in the box. Your work may include a drawing.
5. Write your answer on the line.
6. Write your answer as a complete sentence.

Planes, Trains, & Automobiles

Add & Subtract: 5-Digit

1. Last year, 15,221 students rode the bus in September and 11,115 students rode the bus in October. How many more students rode the bus in September than in October?

    A. 15,221 + 15,221 =

    B. 15,221 + 11,115 =

    C. 11,115 – 11,115 =

    D. 15,221 – 11,115 =

    Answer: _____

    Sentence: _____

Show Your Work

2. On Monday, 67,001 people took the train to work. On Friday, 48,987 people took the train to work. How many more people took the train to work on Monday than on Friday?

    A. 67,001 – 48,987 =

    B. 48,987 + 48,987 =

    C. 67,001 + 48,987 =

    D. 67,001 + 67,001 =

    Answer: _____

    Sentence: _____

Show Your Work

Name _____

3. A small airline had 89,425 passengers during the first half of the year and 93,596 passengers during the second half of the year. How many passengers did the airline have in all during the entire year?

   A. 93,596 + 93,596 =

   B. 93,596 − 89,425 =

   C. 93,596 − 93,596 =

   D. 93,596 + 89,425 =

   Answer: _____

   Sentence: _____

   _____

Show Your Work

4. At the start of the summer, Mr. Hart's car had 36,471 miles on it. At the end of the summer, his car had 40,320 miles on it. How many miles did Mr. Hart drive his car during the entire summer?

   A. 36,471 − 36,471 =

   B. 40,320 + 36,471 =

   C. 40,320 − 36,471 =

   D. 40,320 − 40,471 =

   Answer: _____

   Sentence: _____

Show Your Work

Name _____

5. People traveled by car, train, and bus
    to visit Happyville State Park during the
    summer. Of the summer visitors, 17,987
    traveled 100 miles or less to reach the park
    and 21,009 traveled more than 100 miles.
    How many people visited the Happyville
    State Park in all during the summer?

    A. $17,987 - 200 =$

    B. $21,009 + 17,987 =$

    C. $21,009 - 17,987 =$

    D. $21,009 + 100 + 100 =$

    Answer: _____

    Sentence: _____

    _____

Show Your Work

Instant Assessment Checklist

Problem Number	Facts Underlined	Number Sentence Chosen	Work Shown	Answer Written	Sentence Completed
1					
2					
3					
4					
5					

Name _____

Travel Expenses

Add & Subtract: Money

1. Reid wants to visit his friend in Texas. Reid determines it will cost $375.00 to fly and $119.00 to go by bus. How much more will it cost Reid to travel by airplane than by bus?

   A. $375.00 + $119.00 =

   B. $375.00 − $375.00 =

   C. $375.00 − $119.00 =

   D. $119.00 + $119.00 =

   Answer: _____

   Sentence: _____

Show Your Work

2. April and her mom and dad are going on vacation to Wonderland Park. Tickets to the park cost $89.00 for an adult and $55.00 for a child. How much will the tickets cost altogether for April's family to go to Wonderland Park?

   A. $89.00 + $55.00 + $55.00 =

   B. $89.00 − $55.00 =

   C. $89.00 + $89.00 + $89.00 =

   D. $89.00 + $89.00 + $55.00 =

   Answer: _____

   Sentence: _____

Show Your Work

Name _____

Add & Subtract: Money

3. Mr. Lambert bought a $238.99 ticket at the airport to travel to California for a Los Angeles Lakers game. Then, he spent $17.50 at the airport store on a snack and a magazine. How much money did Mr. Lambert spend at the airport altogether?

    A. $238.99 – $17.50 =

    B. $238.99 + $17.50 =

    C. $238.00 + $17.00 =

    D. $238.99 – $238.99 =

    Answer: _____

    Sentence: _____

    _____

> **Show Your Work**

4. Mrs. Juarez stayed at a hotel for two nights on her business trip. If the first night cost $58.55 and the total bill for both nights was $139.95, how much did the second night at the hotel cost?

    A. $58.55 + $58.55 =

    B. $139.95 – $139.95 =

    C. $139.95 + $58.55 =

    D. $139.95 – $58.55 =

    Answer: _____

    Sentence: _____

> **Show Your Work**

Name _____

5. Kahlil takes the train to visit his dad for the summer. It costs $135.68 for the train ticket there and $129.48 for the return ticket. How much does Kahlil's train trip cost total?

    A. $135.68 + $135.68 =

    B. $135.68 – $129.48 =

    C. $135.68 + $129.48 =

    D. $135.68 – $135.68 =

Answer: _____

Sentence: _____

_____

Show Your Work

Instant Assessment Checklist

Problem Number	Facts Underlined	Number Sentence Chosen	Work Shown	Answer Written	Sentence Completed
1					
2					
3					
4					
5					

Name _____

Team Players

Multiply: 1-Digit

Number of Players Needed

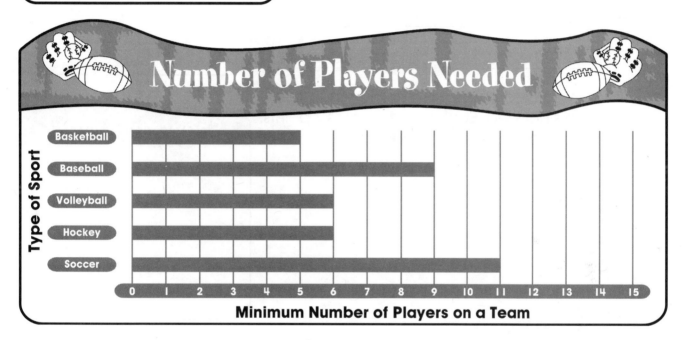

Use the graph to answer the following questions.

1. How many basketball players are on the court during a game?

   A. 2 x 5 =

   B. 5 x 5 =

   C. 5 x 1 =

   D. 2 x 6 =

   Answer: _____

   Sentence: _____

Show Your Work

Name _____

2. There are 8 teams in Alvin's baseball league. At least how many players are in the league?

   A. $8 \times 8 =$

   B. $8 \times 9 =$

   C. $6 \times 8 =$

   D. $9 \times 9 =$

   Answer: _____

   Sentence: _____

   _____

Show Your Work

3. A volleyball team has the minimum number of players needed. Each player makes 7 points. How many points does the team make?

   A. $5 \times 7 =$

   B. $9 \times 7 =$

   C. $6 \times 8 =$

   D. $6 \times 7 =$

   Answer: _____

   Sentence: _____

Show Your Work

4. Trey is starting a basketball club with 6 teams. At least how many players need to join?

   A. $9 \times 6 =$

   B. $6 \times 6 =$

   C. $6 \times 5 =$

   D. $5 \times 5 =$

   Answer: _____

   Sentence: _____

Show Your Work

Name _____

5. On Saturday, 4 hockey teams practiced at the ice rink before the playoffs. If only the starting players practiced, how many players in all practiced for the playoffs at the ice rink on Saturday?

Multiply: 1-Digit

A. 2 x 2 =

B. 6 x 6 =

C. 4 x 6 =

D. 2 x 6 =

Answer: _____

Sentence: _____

_____

Show Your Work

Instant Assessment Checklist

Problem Number	Facts Underlined	Number Sentence Chosen	Work Shown	Answer Written	Sentence Completed
1					
2					
3					
4					
5					

Name _____

Directions:
1. Read the word problem.
2. Underline the facts you will need to solve the problem.
3. Circle the letter beside the number sentence you should use to solve the problem.
4. Solve the problem. Show your work in the box. Your work may include a drawing.
5. Write your answer on the line.
6. Write your answer as a complete sentence.

On the Team Bus

Multiply: 1-Digit

1. There are 8 rows of seats on the bus. Each row has 4 seats. How many seats are on the bus altogether?

    A. 8 x 8 =

    B. 8 x 4 =

    C. 8 + 4 =

    D. 4 x 6 =

    Answer: _____

    Sentence: _____

    Show Your Work

2. There are 3 groups of basketball players on the bus wearing hats and 2 groups not wearing hats. If there are 5 players in each group, how many basketball players on the bus are wearing hats?

    A. 3 x 2 =

    B. 3 x 5 =

    C. 5 x 5 =

    D. 5 x 2 =

    Answer: _____

    Sentence: _____

    Show Your Work

Name _____

Multiply: 1-Digit

3. There are 2 chaperones on the bus for each group of 6 team members. There are 7 groups of team members. How many chaperones are on the bus in all?

    A. 7 x 2 =

    B. 6 x 2 =

    C. 7 x 6 =

    D. 7 x 7 =

    Answer: _____

    Sentence: _____

    _____

Show Your Work

4. The team loads 3 bags of equipment on the bus. If there are 9 towels in each bag, how many towels are in all 3 bags combined?

    A. 9 x 9 =

    B. 9 − 3 =

    C. 3 x 3 =

    D. 3 x 9 =

    Answer: _____

    Sentence: _____

Show Your Work

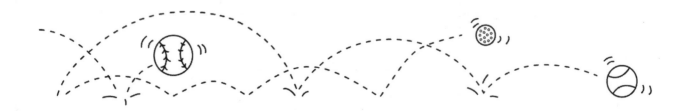

Name _____

5. The 4 coaches each bring a cooler on the bus. Each cooler contains 7 bottles of water. How many bottles of water are in the coolers in all?

    A. 7 x 7 =

    B. 4 x 7 =

    C. 4 x 4 =

    D. 7 x 2 =

    Answer: _____

    Sentence: _____

    _____

Show Your Work

Instant Assessment Checklist

Problem Number	Facts Underlined	Number Sentence Chosen	Work Shown	Answer Written	Sentence Completed
1					
2					
3					
4					
5					

Name _____

Directions:
1. Read the word problem.
2. Underline the facts you will need to solve the problem.
3. Circle the letter beside the number sentence you should use to solve the problem.
4. Solve the problem. Show your work in the box. Your work may include a drawing.
5. Write your answer on the line.
6. Write your answer as a complete sentence.

Sports & the Smiths

Multiply: 1-Digit

1. In the Smiths' garage, there are 3 bags of soccer balls. If 8 soccer balls are in each bag, how many soccer balls are in the bags in all?

    A. $8 \times 6 =$

    B. $8 - 3 =$

    C. $3 \times 3 =$

    D. $3 \times 8 =$

    Answer: _____

    Show Your Work

    Sentence: _____

2. Mike Smith's dad drives him a total of 9 miles to soccer camp every day. How many miles does Mike's dad drive him to soccer camp in 1 week?

    A. $1 \times 7 =$

    B. $8 \times 9 =$

    C. $7 \times 7 =$

    D. $7 \times 9 =$

    Answer: _____

    Show Your Work

    Sentence: _____

Name _____

3. The Smith family has 6 cans of tennis balls
    and 5 tennis rackets. Each can of tennis balls
    has 3 balls in it. How many tennis balls are in
    the 6 cans altogether?

    A. 6 x 3 =

    B. 3 x 3 =

    C. 6 x 6 =

    D. 5 x 6 =

    Answer: _____

    Sentence: _____

    _____

Show Your Work

4. There are 4 soccer players in the Smith
    family. Mrs. Smith buys each player 2 pairs of
    cleats during the season. How many pairs of
    cleats does Mrs. Smith buy for all 4 soccer
    players in her family?

    A. 4 x 4 =

    B. 4 x 2 =

    C. 4 x 6 =

    D. 6 + 4 =

    Answer: _____

    Sentence: _____

Show Your Work

Name _____

5. The Smiths try to keep their sports gear organized in 5 baskets beside the front door. They keep 9 sports items in each basket. How many total pieces of sports gear are in the 5 baskets?

A. 5 x 5 =

B. 9 + 5 =

C. 5 x 9 =

D. 9 x 9 =

Answer: _____

Sentence: _____

_____

Show Your Work

Instant Assessment Checklist

Problem Number	Facts Underlined	Number Sentence Chosen	Work Shown	Answer Written	Sentence Completed
1					
2					
3					
4					
5					

Name _____

Directions:
1. Read the word problem.
2. Underline the facts you will need to solve the problem.
3. Circle the letter beside the number sentence you should use to solve the problem.
4. Solve the problem. Show your work in the box. Your work may include a drawing.
5. Write your answer on the line.
6. Write your answer as a complete sentence.

The Rides

Multiply: 2-Digit x 1-Digit

1. There are 18 cars in the bumper-car ride. If 2 people can ride in each car, how many people can ride at the same time?

   A. 18 x 2 =

   B. 18 + 2 =

   C. 18 – 2 =

   D. 8 x 2 =

   Answer: _____

   Sentence: _____

Show Your Work

2. The Ferris wheel has 15 seats. Each seat can hold up to 4 people. What is the maximum number of people that can ride the Ferris wheel at any time?

   A. 15 x 2 =

   B. 15 x 4 =

   C. 15 x 15 =

   D. 15 – 4 =

   Answer: _____

   Sentence: _____

Show Your Work

Name _____

3. There are 4 lines of people waiting to ride the big roller coaster. There are 55 people in each line, and the wait time from the end of each line is about 35 minutes. How many people are in all 4 lines?

    A. 55 − 35 =

    B. 55 x 35 =

    C. 55 x 4 =

    D. 35 x 4 =

    Answer: _____

    Sentence: _____

    _____

Show Your Work

4. The Swinging Airplanes is one of the most popular rides at the carnival. It runs 48 times a day. The maximum number of people the ride can hold at a time is 9. How many people ride the Swinging Airplanes on a day if it is full each time it runs?

    A. 48 x 48 =

    B. 48 x 9 =

    C. 48 + 9 =

    D. 9 x 9 =

    Answer: _____

    Sentence: _____

Show Your Work

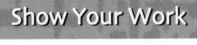

Name _____

5. Benjamin spends 8 hours at the carnival on Saturday afternoon. Benjamin rides the train through the haunted house a total of 16 times. He spends 5 tickets each time he rides. How many tickets does Benjamin spend riding the train through the haunted house?

    A. 16 + 5 =

    B. 8 x 5 =

    C. 16 x 5 =

    D. 16 x 8 =

    Answer: _____

    Sentence: _____

    _____

Show Your Work

Instant Assessment Checklist

Problem Number	Facts Underlined	Number Sentence Chosen	Work Shown	Answer Written	Sentence Completed
1					
2					
3					
4					
5					

Name _____

Directions:
1. Read the word problem.
2. Underline the facts you will need to solve the problem.
3. Circle the letter beside the number sentence you should use to solve the problem.
4. Solve the problem. Show your work in the box. Your work may include a drawing.
5. Write your answer on the line.
6. Write your answer as a complete sentence.

The Treats

Multiply: 3-Digit x 1-Digit

1. There are 6 hot-dog stands at the carnival. On Friday night, each hot-dog stand sold 104 hot dogs. How many hot dogs were sold in all on Friday night?

    A. 6 x 6 =

    B. 104 – 6 =

    C. 104 + 104 =

    D. 104 x 6 =

    Answer: _____

    Sentence: _____

Show Your Work

2. Shaketha and Rachel each buy a bag of peanuts at the carnival. There are 175 peanuts in each bag. How many peanuts do Shaketha and Rachel have altogether?

    A. 175 + 2 =

    B. 175 – 2 =

    C. 175 x 175 =

    D. 175 x 2 =

    Answer: _____

    Sentence: _____

Show Your Work

Name _____

3. The carnival is in town for 9 days. Each day during the carnival, 366 caramel apples and 252 candy apples are sold. How many caramel apples are sold during all 9 days?

    A. 366 x 9 =

    B. 366 + 9 =

    C. 252 x 9 =

    D. 366 – 252 =

    Answer: _____

    Sentence: _____

    _____

Show Your Work

4. Sarah's mother works at the ice-cream stand during the carnival. On 4 different nights, Sarah helps her mom at the stand. Each time Sarah works, the stand sells a total of 199 sundaes. How many sundaes does the ice-cream stand sell in all during the 4 nights that Sarah is there?

    A. 4 x 4 =

    B. 199 + 4 =

    C. 199 x 199 =

    D. 199 x 4 =

    Answer: _____

    Sentence: _____

Show Your Work

Name _____

5. The hot-pretzel vendor makes $285 a day at the carnival. He is only open on Friday, Saturday, and Sunday during the 9-day run of the carnival. How much money does the hot-pretzel vendor make in all?

    A. 3 x 9 =

    B. $285 x 9 =

    C. $285 + $285 =

    D. $285 x 3 =

    Answer: _____

    Sentence: _____

    _____

Show Your Work

Instant Assessment Checklist

Problem Number	Facts Underlined	Number Sentence Chosen	Work Shown	Answer Written	Sentence Completed
1					
2					
3					
4					
5					

Name _____

Directions:
1. Read the word problem.
2. Underline the facts you will need to solve the problem.
3. Circle the letter beside the number sentence you should use to solve the problem.
4. Solve the problem. Show your work in the box. Your work may include a drawing.
5. Write your answer on the line.
6. Write your answer as a complete sentence.

Hanging Out with Friends

Multiply: 2-Digit x 2-Digit

1. There are 16 birthday parties at the carnival. If 20 children (including the birthday child) attend each party, how many children will attend a birthday party at the carnival?

   A. $2 \times 16 =$

   B. $16 \times 20 =$

   C. $16 \times 16 =$

   D. $20 - 16 =$

   Answer:_____

   Sentence: _____

   Show Your Work

2. A group of 15 friends buys tickets for the carnival rides and food. Each friend buys 48 tickets. How many tickets does the group of friends buy in all?

   A. $48 \times 48 =$

   B. $15 \times 15 =$

   C. $48 \times 15 =$

   D. $48 - 15 =$

   Answer:_____

   Sentence: _____

   Show Your Work

Name _____

3. Emory invites his 27 classmates to go to the carnival with him. While they are there, each classmate (including Emory) rides 23 rides. How many rides do the classmates ride at the carnival altogether?

A. 28 x 23 =

B. 28 – 23 =

C. 28 x 28 =

D. 23 x 23 =

Answer: _____

Sentence: _____

_____

Show Your Work

4. A group of 12 friends visits the carnival. They each have 35 coins to spend at the carnival arcade. How many coins do the friends have to spend altogether?

A. 35 + 12 =

B. 12 x 12 =

C. 35 x 12 =

D. 35 x 35 =

Answer: _____

Sentence: _____

Show Your Work

Name _____

5.   On "Friends and Family Day" at the carnival, 98 friends and family members received free admission to the carnival because they brought cans of food to donate to a shelter. If each person brought 23 cans, how many cans were donated in all?

   A. 23 x 23 =

   B. 98 x 23 =

   C. 98 − 23 =

   D. 98 + 23 =

   Answer: _____

   Sentence: _____

   _____

Show Your Work

Instant Assessment Checklist

Problem Number	Facts Underlined	Number Sentence Chosen	Work Shown	Answer Written	Sentence Completed
1					
2					
3					
4					
5					

Name _____

Directions:
1. Read the word problem.
2. Underline the facts you will need to solve the problem.
3. Circle the letter beside the number sentence you should use to solve the problem.
4. Solve the problem. Show your work in the box. Your work may include a drawing.
5. Write your answer on the line.
6. Write your answer as a complete sentence.

Getting Fit

Divide: 1-Digit Divisor
(no remainder)

1. Nina is in a 10-kilometer race on Saturday. She knows there is a water station halfway through the race. How many kilometers will Nina run before she can stop at the water station?

   A. $10 \div 2 =$

   B. $10 \times 2 =$

   C. $10 \div 4 =$

   D. $10 + 2 =$

   Answer: _____

   Sentence: _____

Show Your Work

2. Jorge swims every day after school. He swims a total of 35 miles each week. If he swims an equal number of miles after school each day, how many miles does Jorge swim on Wednesday?

   A. $7 \times 5 =$

   B. $35 \div 5 =$

   C. $35 \div 7 =$

   D. $25 \div 5 =$

   Answer: _____

   Sentence: _____

Show Your Work

Name _____

3. Brandy exercises every day at the gym. She uses the treadmill for 30 minutes, and she does 115 sit-ups in 5 minutes. If Brandy does the same number of sit-ups each minute, how many sit-ups does she do per minute?

    A. 30 x 5 =

    B. 30 ÷ 5 =

    C. 115 ÷ 5 =

    D. 115 ÷ 30 =

    Answer: _____

    Sentence: _____

    _____

Show Your Work

4. Miss Carter spends 28 hours teaching aerobics classes during a 7-day period. She teaches an equal number of hours each day. How many hours of aerobics does Miss Carter teach each day?

    A. 28 x 7 =

    B. 28 + 7 =

    C. 28 ÷ 28 =

    D. 28 ÷ 7 =

    Answer: _____

    Sentence: _____

Show Your Work

Name _____

Divide: 1-Digit Divisor (no remainder)

5. Darius is organizing the gym. He is putting 63 weights on shelves. There are 3 shelves on the wall, and he wants to place an equal number of weights on each shelf. How many weights should Darius place on each shelf?

   A. 63 ÷ 2 =

   B. 63 x 3 =

   C. 63 ÷ 3 =

   D. 63 – 3 =

   Answer: _____

   Sentence: _____

   _____

Show Your Work

Instant Assessment Checklist

Problem Number	Facts Underlined	Number Sentence Chosen	Work Shown	Answer Written	Sentence Completed
1					
2					
3					
4					
5					

Name _____

Fitness Challenge

Divide: 2-Digit Divisor (no remainder)

1. The recreation center is hosting a fitness challenge. There are 240 people participating on 10 teams. If each team is equal in number, how many people are on each team?

   A. $240 \div 5 =$

   B. $240 \div 10 =$

   C. $240 \times 10 =$

   D. $240 \div 2 =$

   Answer: _____

   Sentence: _____

   Show Your Work

2. A free-throw contest is scheduled at 2 P.M. on Saturday for 48 participants. If 432 shots are attempted during the contest and each person attempted the same number of shots, how many shots did each person attempt?

   A. $432 \times 48 =$

   B. $432 \div 2 =$

   C. $432 \div 42 =$

   D. $432 \div 48 =$

   Answer: _____

   Sentence: _____

   Show Your Work

Name _____

Divide: 2-Digit Divisor (no remainder)

3. At the recreation center, there are 12 stations set up for the chin-up competition. If all of the participants in the fitness challenge compete and an equal number go to each station, how many participants will compete at each chin-up station? (Hint: refer to #1.)

    A. 240 ÷ 12 =

    B. 10 x 12 =

    C. 240 ÷ 10 =

    D. 240 x 12 =

    Answer: _____

    Sentence: _____

    _____

Show Your Work

4. Of the participants, 144 signed up for a healthy habits seminar. Because so many people signed up, they decided to hold 12 sessions and have an equal number of people attend each session. How many people will attend each session?

    A. 144 ÷ 4 =

    B. 144 ÷ 12 =

    C. 144 ÷ 2 =

    D. 12 x 12 =

    Answer: _____

    Sentence: _____

Show Your Work

Name _____

5. Tam Lee needs to order 286 certificates for all of the fitness challenge participants and volunteers. The certificates come in packages of 13. How many packages of certificates will Tam Lee need to order?

   A. 13 ÷ 13 =

   B. 286 − 240 =

   C. 286 ÷ 13 =

   D. 286 x 13 =

   Answer: _____

   Sentence: _____

   _____

Show Your Work

Instant Assessment Checklist

Problem Number	Facts Underlined	Number Sentence Chosen	Work Shown	Answer Written	Sentence Completed
1					
2					
3					
4					
5					

Name _____

Directions:
1. Read the word problem.
2. Underline the facts you will need to solve the problem.
3. Circle the letter beside the number sentence you should use to solve the problem.
4. Solve the problem. Show your work in the box. Your work may include a drawing.
5. Write your answer on the line.
6. Write your answer as a complete sentence.

Daily Exercise

Divide: 1-Digit Divisor (remainder)

1. Dave bicycles 29 miles during a 3-day period. He bicycles about the same number of miles during each of the 3 days. About how many miles does Dave bicycle each day?

   A. 29 x 3 =

   B. 29 ÷ 3 =

   C. 3 ÷ 3 =

   D. 29 – 3 =

   Answer:_____

   Sentence: _____

   Show Your Work

2. A special deal at the health club allows Holly to pay $55 for a 2-month membership. About how much does it cost Holly each month to belong to the health club?

   A. $55 ÷ 5 =

   B. $55 x 2 =

   C. $55 x 60 =

   D. $55 ÷ 2 =

   Answer:_____

   Sentence: _____

   Show Your Work

Name _____

3. Orlando has $79. Every day of the week, he spends the same amount of money for a personal trainer at the gym. At the end of the week, he wants to reward himself for his hard work. How much money does he have left to spend on his reward?

    A. $79 ÷ 7 =

    B. $79 ÷ 4 =

    C. $79 − 7 =

    D. 7 x $79 =

    Answer: _____

    Sentence: _____

    _____

Show Your Work

4. Amber spends 19 hours on the stair-stepping machine over a 9-day period. She spends about the same amount of time on the machine every day. About how many hours does Amber spend on the stair-stepping machine each day?

    A. 19 x 9 =

    B. 9 ÷ 9 =

    C. 19 ÷ 10 =

    D. 19 ÷ 9 =

    Answer: _____

    Sentence: _____

Show Your Work

Name _____

5. Brian is training for a race. Brian's goal is to run a total of 100 miles before the race. If he runs 8 miles a day, how many days will Brian need to run to reach his goal?

    A. 100 ÷ 100 =

    B. 100 x 8 =

    C. 100 ÷ 8 =

    D. 100 + 8 =

    Answer: _____

    Sentence: _____

    _____

Show Your Work

Instant Assessment Checklist

Problem Number	Facts Underlined	Number Sentence Chosen	Work Shown	Answer Written	Sentence Completed
1					
2					
3					
4					
5					

Name _____

Directions:
1. Read the word problem.
2. Underline the facts you will need to solve the problem.
3. Circle the letter beside the number sentence you should use to solve the problem.
4. Solve the problem. Show your work in the box. Your work may include a drawing.
5. Write your answer on the line.
6. Write your answer as a complete sentence.

Healthy Habits

Divide: 1-Digit Divisor (remainder)

1. Latosha is famous for her all-natural cookies. She uses a box of 136 raisins to make 1 batch of cookies. If there are 9 cookies in each batch and she puts an equal number of raisins in each cookie, how many raisins are in 1 cookie?

   A. 13 x 13 =

   B. 136 x 14 =

   C. 136 ÷ 9 =

   D. 136 ÷ 136 =

   Answer: _____

   Sentence: _____

Show Your Work

2. Mr. Cooper operates the Veggie Burger Stand for 8 hours every day. He sold 220 veggie burgers on Saturday, selling about the same number per hour. About how many burgers per hour did he sell?

   A. 220 x 8 =

   B. 220 ÷ 8 =

   C. 220 − 8 =

   D. 8 x 8 =

   Answer: _____

   Sentence: _____

Show Your Work

Name _____

3. Mrs. Poitras has 6 children. She divides 88 yogurt raisins into bags for her children to take to school as a snack. She puts an equal number of yogurt raisins in each child's bag and eats the leftover raisins. How many yogurt raisins does Mrs. Poitras put in each bag? How many raisins does she eat?

    A. 88 ÷ 5 =

    B. 88 x 6 =

    C. 88 ÷ 6 =

    D. 88 ÷ 8 =

    Answer: _____

    Sentence: _____

    _____

Show Your Work

4. For a healthy snack after the track meet, 6 runners divide 112 grapes equally. Their coach eats the remaining grapes. How many grapes does each player eat? How many grapes are left for their coach?

    A. 112 x 6 =

    B. 112 ÷ 4 =

    C. 112 ÷ 112 =

    D. 112 ÷ 6 =

    Answer: _____

    Sentence: _____

Show Your Work

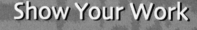

5. The Carlile family drinks 135 bottles of mineral water every week. The bottles come in packs of 8. How many packs does Mr. Carlile need to buy at the start of each week?

A. $135 \div 8 =$

B. $135 \div 4 =$

C. $135 \times 8 =$

D. $135 - 8 =$

Answer: _____

Sentence: _____

_____

Show Your Work

Instant Assessment Checklist

Problem Number	Facts Underlined	Number Sentence Chosen	Work Shown	Answer Written	Sentence Completed
1					
2					
3					
4					
5					

Name _____

Directions:
1. Read the word problem.
2. Underline the facts you will need to solve the problem.
3. Circle the letter beside the number sentence you should use to solve the problem.
4. Solve the problem. Show your work in the box. Your work may include a drawing.
5. Write your answer on the line.
6. Write your answer as a complete sentence.

Penny's Problems

Multistep Problems

1. Penny has $25 on Friday. She does several chores over the weekend and doubles her money. If she spends $14 at the movies, how much money does Penny have now?

   A. $25 x 2 =   then $50 – $25 =

   B. $14 x 2 =   then $28 – $25 =

   C. $25 + $14 =   then $39 x 2 =

   D. $25 x 2 =   then $50 – $14 =

   Show Your Work

   Answer: _____

   Sentence: _____

2. Penny has 54 buttons. She divides them into 6 equal groups. Then, she adds 18 new buttons to each group. How many buttons are in each group now?

   A. 54 x 6 =   then   324 + 18 =

   B. 54 ÷ 6 =   then   9 + 18 =

   C. 18 + 6 =   then   54 – 24 =

   D. 54 ÷ 6 =   then   18 – 9 =

   Show Your Work

   Answer: _____

   Sentence: _____

Name _____

3. Penny buys 19 new games for her pocket game-player. She now has 85 games. Penny's cousin has 3 times as many games as Penny had before her recent purchase. How many games does Penny's cousin have?

A. 85 + 19 =   then   104 x 3 =

B. 85 x 3 =   then   255 + 19 =

C. 85 – 19 =   then   66 x 3 =

D. 85 – 19 =   then   66 ÷ 3 =

Answer: _____

Sentence: _____

_____

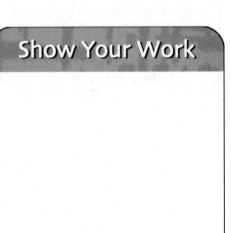

Show Your Work

4. There are 1,289 students enrolled at each of the 2 elementary schools in Penny's town. Throughout the school year, 189 students move away and no new students move to the town. How many students are enrolled at the 2 schools in Penny's town at the end of the school year?

A. 1,289 + 1,289 =   then   2,578 – 189 =

B. 1,289 – 1,289 =   then   189 – 0 =

C. 1,289 + 1,289 =   then   2,578 + 189 =

D. 1,289 + 189 =   then   1,478 – 189 =

Answer: _____

Show Your Work

Sentence: _____

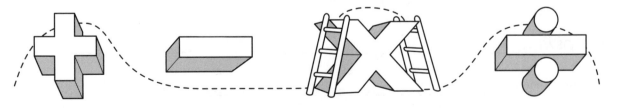

Name _____

5. Penny's teacher asks for her help to figure out how many eggs to buy for an egg-dying party. Her teacher wants to divide the children into groups of 3 and give each group a dozen eggs. How many eggs should Penny tell her teacher to buy if there are 45 students in the class?

A. $45 + 12 =$ then $57 \div 3 =$

B. $45 \div 3 =$ then $15 \times 12 =$

C. $45 \times 3 =$ then $135 \times 12 =$

D. $45 \times 12 =$ then $540 \times 3 =$

Answer: _____

Sentence: _____

_____

Show Your Work

Instant Assessment Checklist

Problem Number	Facts Underlined	Number Sentence Chosen	Work Shown	Answer Written	Sentence Completed
1					
2					
3					
4					
5					

Name _____

Directions:
1. Read the word problem.
2. Underline the facts you will need to solve the problem.
3. Circle the letter beside the number sentence you should use to solve the problem.
4. Solve the problem. Show your work in the box. Your work may include a drawing.
5. Write your answer on the line.
6. Write your answer as a complete sentence.

Spending & Saving

Multistep Problems

1. Tasha earned $18.35 baby-sitting. Her sister, Tonya, earned twice as much from her baby-sitting job. Tonya decides to save $20.00 and spend the rest. How much money does Tonya have left to spend?

   A. $18.35 + $20.00 = then $38.35 ÷ 2 =

   B. $18.35 x 2 =   then $36.70 − $20.00 =

   C. $20.00 x 2 =   then $40.00 x 2 =

   D. $20.00 − $18.35 =   then $1.65 x 2 =

   Show Your Work

   Answer: _____

   Sentence: _____

2. Jake earns $14.29 on Thursday and $27.55 on Saturday. He puts half the money he earns in his savings account and spends the rest. How much money does Jake put in savings?

   A. $14.29 + $27.55 = then $41.84 x 2 =

   B. $27.55 − $14.29 = then $13.26 x 2 =

   C. $14.29 + $14.29 = then $28.58 ÷ 2 =

   D. $14.29 + $27.55 = then $41.84 ÷ 2 =

   Show Your Work

   Answer: _____

   Sentence: _____

Name _____

Multistep Problems

3. Terri mows lawns during June. She earns a total of $99.00 mowing lawns. She spends $16.80 on gas, trash bags, and other supplies. She sends in a rebate coupon on the trash bags and receives a check for $2.50 in the mail. How much money does Terri have now?

A. $99.00 – $16.80 =   then $82.20 – $2.50 =
B. $99.00 – $16.80 =   then $82.20 + $2.50 =
C. $99.00 + $16.80 =   then $115.80 + $2.50 =
D. $16.80 + $2.50 =   then $19.30 + $99.00 =

Answer: _____

Sentence: _____

_____

Show Your Work

4. Three sisters count the money they have saved in their piggy banks. Amy has $6. Her sister Leanne has saved 5 times as much money, and her other sister Jen has saved a third as much money as Leanne. How much money does Jen have in her piggy bank?

A. $6 + 5 =   then $11 x 3 =
B. $6 x 5 =   then $30 ÷ 3 =
C. $6 x 3 =   then $18 x 5 =
D. 5 x 3 =   then   15 x $6 =

Answer: _____

Sentence: _____

Show Your Work

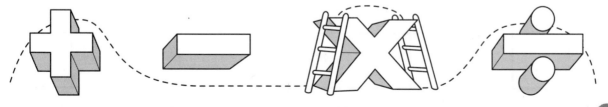

Multistep Problems

5. Maria spends some money while she is on vacation. She spends a total of $56.34 on food and $27.99 on souvenirs. Maria returns home with $15.67. How much money did Maria have when she left to go on vacation?

A. $27.99 + $15.67 =   then $56.34 – $43.66 =
B. $56.34 – $15.67 =   then $40.67 + $56.34 =
C. $56.34 – $27.99 =   then $28.35 + $15.67 =
D. $56.34 + $27.99 =   then $84.33 + $15.67 =

Answer: _____

Sentence: _____

_____

Show Your Work

Instant Assessment Checklist

Problem Number	Facts Underlined	Number Sentence Chosen	Work Shown	Answer Written	Sentence Completed
1					
2					
3					
4					
5					

Name _____

Summer Camp

Multistep Problems

1. Jamal is at camp for 3 weeks during the summer. Each day, he spends 20 minutes practicing archery. How many minutes in all does Jamal spend practicing archery at camp?

    A. 3 x 20 =   then   60 x 3 =

    B. 3 x 7 =   then   21 x 20 =

    C. 20 + 3 =   then   23 x 7 =

    D. 7 x 3 =   then   21 + 20 =

    Answer: _____

    Sentence: _____

    Show Your Work

2. Jan has saved $67 to pay for camp. She needs 4 times as much money as she has to pay the camp fee. Right before registration, Jan still needs $15, which her mother pays. How much money does Jan contribute to pay for camp?

    A. $67 x 4 =   then $268 x $15 =

    B. $67 + 4 =   then $71 − $15 =

    C. $67 x 4 =   then $268 − $15 =

    D. $67 x 4 =   then $268 + $15 =

    Answer: _____

    Sentence: _____

    Show Your Work

Name _____

3. There are 56 campers at Camp Summer Fun. Monica is on a team of 8 campers. Each team will receive 12 team awards by the end of camp. How many team awards will be given out in all by the end of camp?

    A. 56 ÷ 8 =   then   7 x 12 =

    B. 56 x 8 =   then   448 x 12 =

    C. 56 ÷ 8 =   then   7 + 12 =

    D. 12 – 8 =   then   56 x 4 =

    Answer: _____

    Sentence: _____

    _____

Show Your Work

4. Greg has $15.00 to spend at camp. He spends $11.54 on postcards, stamps, and candy at the camp's convenience store. Then, his grandmother sends him cookies and $8.75 in a care package. How much money does Greg have now?

    A. $15.00 – $8.75 =   then $6.25 + $11.54 =

    B. $15.00 – $11.54 =   then $8.75 – $3.46 =

    C. $15.00 + $11.54 =   then $26.54 + $8.75 =

    D. $15.00 – $11.54 =   then $3.46 + $8.75 =

    Answer: _____

    Sentence: _____

Show Your Work

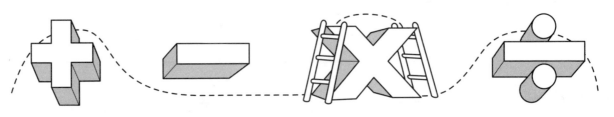

5. Terrell has gone to a 14-day camp for the past 5 summers. Each day at camp, the campers walk 3 miles. How many total miles has Terrell walked at camp?

Multistep Problems

A. 14 x 3 =   then   42 – 5 =

B. 5 x 3 =   then   15 + 14 =

C. 14 x 5 =   then   70 + 3 =

D. 14 x 5 =   then   70 x 3 =

Answer: _____

Sentence: _____

_____

Show Your Work

Instant Assessment Checklist

Problem Number	Facts Underlined	Number Sentence Chosen	Work Shown	Answer Written	Sentence Completed
1					
2					
3					
4					
5					

Name _____

Max's Paper Route

Multistep Problems

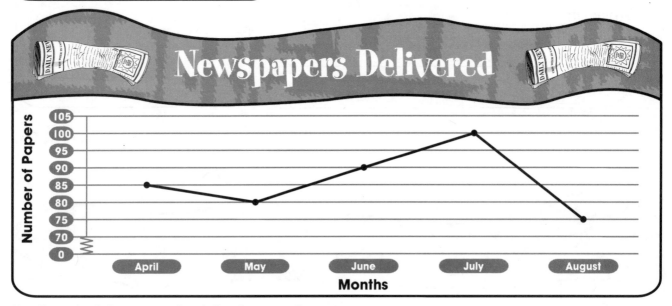

Newspapers Delivered

Number of Papers (y-axis): 105, 100, 95, 90, 85, 80, 75, 70, 0

Months (x-axis): April, May, June, July, August

Use the graph to answer the following questions.

1. During September, Max delivers half as many papers as he delivered in July plus an additional 7 papers. How many papers did Max deliver in September?

   A. $80 \div 2 =$ then $40 - 7 =$

   B. $100 \times 2 =$ then $200 + 7 =$

   C. $100 \div 2 =$ then $50 + 7 =$

   D. $90 \div 2 =$ then $45 - 7 =$

   Answer: _____

   Show Your Work

   Sentence: _____

Name _____

2. Max is competing in a contest. To win, Max needs to deliver 4 times as many papers during a 6-month period as he delivered in May, plus an additional 14 papers. How many papers does Max need to deliver to win the contest?

    A. 80 x 4 =   then   320 + 14 =

    B. 100 x 2 =   then   200 + 7 =

    C. 100 ÷ 2 =   then   50 + 7 =

    D. 90 ÷ 2 =   then   45 – 7 =

    Answer: _____

    Sentence: _____

    Show Your Work

3. In January, Max delivered twice as many papers as he delivered in August, plus 8 more. How many papers did Max deliver in January?

    A. 75 x 2 =   then   150 – 8 =

    B. 85 x 2 =   then   170 + 8 =

    C. 75 x 8 =   then   600 + 2 =

    D. 75 x 2 =   then   150 + 8 =

    Answer: _____

    Sentence: _____

    Show Your Work

4. In March, Max's brother delivered his papers. He delivered 9 fewer than a third as many papers as Max delivered in June. How many papers did Max's brother deliver?

    A. 90 ÷ 3 =   then   30 + 9 =

    B. 90 x 3 =   then   270 – 9 =

    C. 90 ÷ 3 =   then   30 – 9 =

    D. 90 ÷ 9 =   then   10 – 3 =

    Answer: _____

    Sentence: _____

    Show Your Work

Name _____

5. What is the average number of papers that Max delivered over the 5-month period shown on the graph?

Multistep Problems

A. 85 + 80 + 90 + 100 =   then   355 ÷ 4 =
B. 85 + 80 + 90 + 100 + 75 = then   430 ÷ 5 =
C. 85 + 85 + 85 + 85 + 85 =   then   425 ÷ 5 =
D. 85 + 80 + 90 + 100 + 75 = then   430 x 5 =

Answer: _____

Sentence: _____

_____

Show Your Work

Instant Assessment Checklist

Problem Number	Facts Underlined	Number Sentence Chosen	Work Shown	Answer Written	Sentence Completed
1					
2					
3					
4					
5					

Name _____

Directions:
1. Read the word problem.
2. Underline the facts you will need to solve the problem.
3. Circle the letter beside the number sentence you should use to solve the problem.
4. Solve the problem. Show your work in the box. Your work may include a drawing.
5. Write your answer on the line.
6. Write your answer as a complete sentence.

Review

Add & Subtract

1. There are 876 seats in the school auditorium. If 567 of the seats are filled for the assembly and the rest are vacant, how many vacant seats are there?

   A. $876 + 567 =$

   B. $876 - 567 =$

   C. $876 + 876 =$

   D. $567 - 657 =$

   Show Your Work

   Answer: _____

   Sentence: _____

2. The population of Happyville, Arkansas, is 31,411. If 3,293 fewer people live in Jolleyville, Maryland, what is the population of Jolleyville, Maryland?

   A. $31,411 - 31,411 =$

   B. $31,411 - 3,200 =$

   C. $31,411 + 3,293 =$

   D. $31,411 - 3,293 =$

   Show Your Work

   Answer: _____

   Sentence: _____

Name _____

3. Destini keeps track of the money she earns from chores each week of the month. She earns $3.20 the first week, $4.17 the second week, $5.00 the third week, and $3.33 the last week. How much money does Destini earn during the last 2 weeks of the month?

    A. $3.20 + $4.17 + $3.33 =

    B. $3.20 + $3.33 + $5.00 =

    C. $4.17 + $3.33 =

    D. $5.00 + $3.33 =

    Answer:_____

    Sentence: _____

    _____

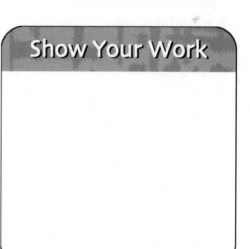

Show Your Work

4. The subway station collected 39,605 tokens on Saturday and 94,217 tokens on Sunday. How many tokens did the subway station collect altogether on both days?

    A. 39,605 + 94,217 =

    B. 39,605 − 39,605 =

    C. 39,605 − 94,217 =

    D. 94,217 + 94,217 =

    Answer:_____

    Sentence: _____

Show Your Work

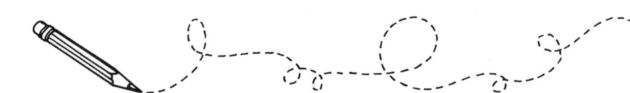

Name _____

5. During September, 2,618 people play miniature golf at Wonderful Hills Miniature Golf Course. During October, 1,006 fewer people play miniature golf there. How many people play miniature golf at Wonderful Hills Miniature Golf Course during October?

A. 2,618 – 2,618 =

B. 2,618 + 1,006 =

C. 2,618 – 1,006 =

D. 2,618 – 1,000 =

Answer: _____

Sentence: _____

_____

Show Your Work

Instant Assessment Checklist

Problem Number	Facts Underlined	Number Sentence Chosen	Work Shown	Answer Written	Sentence Completed
1					
2					
3					
4					
5					

Name _____

Directions:
1. Read the word problem.
2. Underline the facts you will need to solve the problem.
3. Circle the letter beside the number sentence you should use to solve the problem.
4. Solve the problem. Show your work in the box. Your work may include a drawing.
5. Write your answer on the line.
6. Write your answer as a complete sentence.

Review

Multiply: 1-Digit

1. Cally lost 4 teeth this year. The Tooth Fairy gave her $2 for each tooth. How much money did Cally get for her lost teeth this year?

    A. $2 x $2 =

    B. 4 + $2 =

    C. 4 ÷ $2 =

    D. 4 x $2 =

    Answer: _____

    Sentence: _____

Show Your Work

2. Andrew brought 3 lollipops to school for each of his 5 friends. How many lollipops did Andrew bring to school?

    A. 5 x 3 =

    B. 5 x 5 =

    C. 3 x 3 =

    D. 5 + 3 =

    Answer: _____

    Sentence: _____

Show Your Work

© Carson-Dellosa CD-7432

Name _____

3. Carter invited 6 friends to his birthday party. The clown made each child, including Carter, 8 balloon animals. How many balloon animals did the clown make in all?

A. 7 x 8 =

B. 6 x 8 =

C. 8 x 8 =

D. 6 x 6 =

Answer: _____

Sentence: _____

_____

Show Your Work

4. Nikki is buying supplies for the start of the new school year. She will have 9 different subjects and she needs 4 folders for each subject. How many folders does Nikki need to buy?

A. 9 – 4 =

B. 9 x 4 =

C. 9 x 9 =

D. 4 x 4 =

Answer: _____

Sentence: _____

Show Your Work

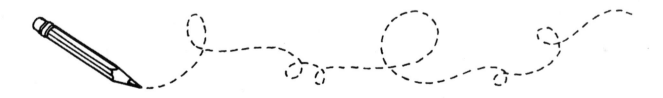

Name _____

5. Paulo does a lot of chores around the house to help out his parents. There are 5 jobs that he does every week. How many jobs does Paulo do each month? (Hint: there are 4 weeks in a month.)

    A. 5 x 5 =

    B. 4 x 5 =

    C. 4 + 5 =

    D. 5 x 1 =

    Answer: _____

    Sentence: _____

    _____

Show Your Work

Instant Assessment Checklist

Problem Number	Facts Underlined	Number Sentence Chosen	Work Shown	Answer Written	Sentence Completed
1					
2					
3					
4					
5					

Name _____

Directions:
1. Read the word problem.
2. Underline the facts you will need to solve the problem.
3. Circle the letter beside the number sentence you should use to solve the problem.
4. Solve the problem. Show your work in the box. Your work may include a drawing.
5. Write your answer on the line.
6. Write your answer as a complete sentence.

Review

Multiply: 2- and 3-Digit

1. There are 94 canoes for rent at a large rental store in Colorado. If each canoe requires 2 paddles, how many paddles are needed for all 94 canoes?

   A. $94 + 2 =$

   B. $94 \div 2 =$

   C. $94 \times 4 =$

   D. $94 \times 2 =$

   Answer: _____

   Sentence: _____

   Show Your Work

2. There are 68 fourth graders registered in the library's Summer Read-a-thon. Each fourth grader reads 12 books. How many books do all 68 fourth graders read altogether?

   A. $68 \times 12 =$

   B. $68 \div 12 =$

   C. $68 + 12 =$

   D. $68 - 12 =$

   Answer: _____

   Sentence: _____

   Show Your Work

Name _____

3. Mr. Brown sells 49 hot pretzels at the park on Wednesday. On a busy Saturday, he sells 6 times as many pretzels as he sold on Wednesday. How many pretzels did Mr. Brown sell on Saturday?

A. 49 ÷ 6 =

B. 49 x 6 =

C. 49 + 49 =

D. 6 x 6 =

Answer:_____

Sentence: _____

_____

Show Your Work

4. Daryl's dad buys 48 cases of lemonade for the pool party. There are 24 cans of lemonade in each case. How many cans of lemonade does Daryl's dad buy in all?

A. 48 x 12 =

B. 48 x 24 =

C. 48 ÷ 24 =

D. 48 − 24 =

Answer:_____

Sentence: _____

Show Your Work

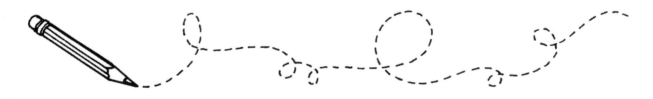

© Carson-Dellosa CD-7432

Name _____

5. Maddy has $115. The tent she wants to purchase costs 3 times the amount of money she currently has. How much does the tent Maddy wants to purchase cost?

    A. $115 + 3 =

    B. $115 ÷ 3 =

    C. $115 x 3 =

    D. $115 − 3 =

    Answer: _____

    Sentence: _____

    _____

Show Your Work

Instant Assessment Checklist

Problem Number	Facts Underlined	Number Sentence Chosen	Work Shown	Answer Written	Sentence Completed
1					
2					
3					
4					
5					

Name _____

Directions:
1. Read the word problem.
2. Underline the facts you will need to solve the problem.
3. Circle the letter beside the number sentence you should use to solve the problem.
4. Solve the problem. Show your work in the box. Your work may include a drawing.
5. Write your answer on the line.
6. Write your answer as a complete sentence.

Review

Divide

1. Mrs. Conner has 64 pencils. She divides them equally between 8 groups of students. How many pencils does each group get?

A. $64 \div 64 =$

B. $64 \div 8 =$

C. $8 \div 8 =$

D. $64 \times 8 =$

Answer: _____

Sentence: _____

Show Your Work

2. Marty has $288. She spends half of her money on a new bike and uses the rest to buy a birthday present for her mom. How much money does Marty spend on her new bike?

A. $\$288 \times 2 =$

B. $\$288 \div 4 =$

C. $\$288 \div 2 =$

D. $\$288 + \$288 =$

Answer: _____

Sentence: _____

Show Your Work

3. Tyree has 84 rocks in his collection. He divides the rocks into 14 equal groups based on their size and color. How many rocks does Tyree put in each group?

   A. 84 + 14 =

   B. 84 x 14 =

   C. 84 ÷ 2 =

   D. 84 ÷ 14 =

   Answer: _____

   Sentence: _____

   _____

Show Your Work

4. Tom's older brother works at a sandwich shop. During his 6-hour shift, he makes a total of 348 sandwiches. Assuming he makes the same number of sandwiches each hour, how many sandwiches does Tom's older brother make each hour that he works?

   A. 348 ÷ 6 =

   B. 348 ÷ 4 =

   C. 348 x 6 =

   D. 348 ÷ 60 =

   Answer: _____

   Sentence: _____

Show Your Work

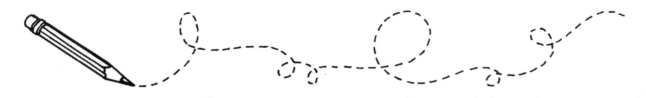

Review
Divide

5. Kami bought a package of balloons to decorate her house for a party. The package contained 50 balloons. She wanted to arrange the balloons in groups of 6 around the house and tie the leftovers to the mailbox. How many groups of 6 balloons will Kami be able to make?
How many balloons will be left to tie to the mailbox?

A. 50 x 6 =

B. 50 ÷ 12 =

C. 50 ÷ 6 =

D. 50 + 6 =

Answer: _____

Sentence: _____

_____

Show Your Work

Instant Assessment Checklist

Problem Number	Facts Underlined	Number Sentence Chosen	Work Shown	Answer Written	Sentence Completed
1					
2					
3					
4					
5					

Name _____

Review

Multistep Problems

1. On Tuesday, Shelby gave away 78 stickers from her sticker collection. On Wednesday, she gave away 67 more stickers. Now she has 345 stickers in her collection. How many stickers did Shelby have before Tuesday?

Show Your Work

A. $345 - 67 =$ then $278 - 78 =$

B. $78 + 76 =$ then $345 - 145 =$

C. $345 + 67 =$ then $412 + 78 =$

D. $345 - 78 =$ then $267 - 67 =$

Answer: _____

Sentence: _____

2. Peter has $28. His brother Sam has half as much money as Peter. His other brother Mel has 4 times as much money as Sam. How much money does Mel have?

Show Your Work

A. $\$28 \div 2 =$ then $\$14 \times 4 =$

B. $\$28 \times 2 =$ then $\$56 \times 4 =$

C. $\$28 \div 2 =$ then $\$14 + 4 =$

D. $\$28 \div 4 =$ then $\$7 \times 2 =$

Answer: _____

Sentence: _____

Name _____

3. Barbara writes the number 624 on a piece of paper. She divides her number by 6. Then, she multiplies her new number by 8. She writes her new number on her piece of paper. What is Barbara's new number?

    A. 624 ÷ 8 =   then   78 x 6 =

    B. 624 ÷ 6 =   then   104 x 8 =

    C. 624 ÷ 6 =   then   104 ÷ 8 =

    D. 624 x 6 =   then   3,744 ÷ 8 =

    Answer: _____

    Sentence: _____

    _____

Show Your Work

4. William knows that 3,456 people live in his town. If 144 people move out of town and 289 people move to town during the fall, how many people live in William's town now?

    A. 3,456 – 144 =   then   3,312 – 289 =

    B. 3,456 + 144 =   then   3,600 + 289 =

    C. 144 + 289 =   then   3,456 + 433 =

    D. 3,456 – 144 =   then   3,312 + 289 =

    Answer: _____

    Sentence: _____

Show Your Work

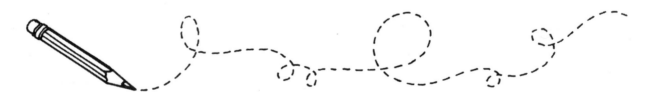

Name _____

5. Charity is on vacation. She takes 34 pictures on Monday. On Tuesday, she takes 18 fewer pictures, and on Wednesday, she takes 6 times as many pictures as she took on Tuesday. How many pictures did Charity take on Wednesday?

A. 34 – 18 =   then   16 + 6 =

B. 34 – 18 =   then   16 x 6 =

C. 34 + 18 =   then   52 x 6 =

D. 34 x 6 =   then   204 + 18 =

Answer:_____

Sentence: _____

_____

Show Your Work

Instant Assessment Checklist

Problem Number	Facts Underlined	Number Sentence Chosen	Work Shown	Answer Written	Sentence Completed
1					
2					
3					
4					
5					

Answer Key

For all problems:

Important facts should be underlined in each problem.
Students' sentences and work will vary.

Pages 7–9

1. A. 327 – 255 =   72 miles
2. B. 170 + 76 =   246 miles
3. B. 578 + 125 =   703 miles
4. D. 254 + 171 + 12 = 437 miles
5. C. 221 – 133 =   88 miles

Pages 10–12

1. B. 1,589 + 1,589 =   3,178 miles
2. D. 5,220 – 3,349 =   1,871 feet
3. B. 6,725 – 2,861 =   3,864 visitors
4. A. 4,250 + 3,955 =   8,205 meters
5. C. 2004 – 1967 =   37 years

Pages 13–15

1. D. 15,221 – 11,115 =   4,106 more students
2. A. 67,001 – 48,987 =   18,014 more people
3. D. 93,596 + 89,425 =   183,021 passengers
4. C. 40,320 – 36,471 =   3,849 miles
5. B. 21,009 + 17,987 =   38,996 people

Pages 16–18

1. C. $375.00 − $119.00 = $256.00
2. D. $89.00 + $89.00 + $55.00 = $233.00
3. B. $238.99 + $17.50 = $256.49
4. D. $139.95 − $58.55 = $81.40
5. C. $135.68 + $129.48 = $265.16

Pages 19–21

1. A. 2 x 5 =   10 basketball players
2. B. 8 x 9 =   72 players
3. D. 6 x 7 =   42 points
4. C. 6 x 5 =   30 players
5. C. 4 x 6 =   24 players

Pages 22–24

1. B. 8 x 4 =   32 seats
2. B. 3 x 5 =   15 basketball players
3. A. 7 x 2 =   14 chaperones
4. D. 3 x 9 =   27 towels
5. B. 4 x 7 =   28 bottles of water

Pages 25–27

1. D. 3 x 8 =   24 soccer balls
2. D. 7 x 9 =   63 miles
3. A. 6 x 3 =   18 tennis balls
4. B. 4 x 2 =   8 pairs of cleats
5. C. 5 x 9 =   45 pieces of sports gear

Pages 28–30

1. A. 18 x 2 =   36 people
2. B. 15 x 4 =   60 people
3. C. 55 x 4 =   220 people
4. B. 48 x 9 =   432 people
5. C. 16 x 5 =   80 tickets

Pages 31–33

1. D. 104 x 6 =   624 hot dogs
2. D. 175 x 2 =   350 peanuts
3. A. 366 x 9 =   3,294 caramel apples
4. D. 199 x 4 =   796 sundaes
5. D. $285 x 3 = $855

Pages 34–36

1. B. 16 x 20 =   320 children
2. C. 48 x 15 =   720 tickets
3. A. 28 x 23 =   644 rides
4. C. 35 x 12 =   420 coins
5. B. 98 x 23 =   2,254 cans

Pages 37–39

1. A. 10 ÷ 2 =   5 kilometers
2. B. 35 ÷ 5 =   7 miles
3. C. 115 ÷ 5 =   23 sit-ups
4. D. 28 ÷ 7 =   4 hours
5. C. 63 ÷ 3 =   21 weights

Pages 40–42

1. B. 240 ÷ 10 =   24 people
2. D. 432 ÷ 48 =   9 shots
3. A. 240 ÷ 12 =   20 participants
4. B. 144 ÷ 12 =   12 people
5. C. 286 ÷ 13 =   22 packages of certificates

Pages 43–45

1. B. 29 ÷ 3 =   about 9 miles (9 R2)
2. D. 55 ÷ 2 =   about $28 (27 R1—round up the $0.50)
3. A. $79 ÷ 7 = $2 (11 R2)
4. D. 19 ÷ 9 =   about 2 hours (2 R1)
5. C. 100 ÷ 8 =   13 days (12 R4)

Answer Key

Pages 46–48

1. C. 136 ÷ 9 =   15 raisins (15 R1)
2. B. 220 ÷ 8 =   about 27 burgers (27 R4)
3. C. 88 ÷ 6 =   14 raisins in each bag/4 raisins eaten (14 R4)
4. D. 112 ÷ 6 =   18 grapes for each player/4 grapes for coach (18 R4)
5. A. 135 ÷ 8 =   17 packs (16 R7)

Pages 49–51

1. D. $25 x 2 =   then $50 – $14 = $36
2. B. 54 ÷ 6 =   then   9 + 18 =   27 buttons
3. C. 85 – 19 =   then   66 x 3 =   198 games
4. A. 1,289 + 1,289 =   then   2,578 – 189 = 2,389 students
5. B. 45 ÷ 3 =   then   15 x 12 =   180 eggs

Pages 52–54

1. B. $18.35 x 2 =   then $36.70 – $20.00 = $16.70
2. D. $14.29 + $27.55 = then $41.84 ÷ 2 = $20.92
3. B. $99.00 – $16.80 = then $82.20 + $2.50 = $84.70
4. B. $6 x 5 =   then $30 ÷ 3 = $10
5. D. $56.34 + $27.99 = then $84.33 + $15.67 = $100.00

Pages 55–57

1. B. 3 x 7 =   then   21 x 20 =   420 minutes
2. C. $67 x 4 =   then $268 – $15 = $253
3. A. 56 ÷ 8 =   then   7 x 12 =   84 team awards
4. D. $15.00 – $11.54 = then $3.46 + $8.75 = $12.21
5. D. 14 x 5 =   then   70 x 3 =   210 miles

Pages 58–60

1. C. 100 ÷ 2 = then   50 + 7 =   57 papers
2. A. 80 x 4 =   then   320 + 14 = 334 papers
3. D. 75 x 2 =   then   150 + 8 =   158 papers
4. C. 90 ÷ 3 =   then   30 – 9 =   21 papers
5. B. 85 + 80 + 90 + 100 + 75 =   then   430 ÷ 5 = 86 papers

Pages 61–63

1. B. 876 – 567 =   309 vacant seats
2. D. 31,411 – 3,293 =   28,118
3. D. $5.00 + $3.33 = $8.33
4. A. 39,605 + 94,217 = 133,822 tokens
5. C. 2,618 – 1,006 =   1,612 people

Pages 64–66

1. D. 4 x $2 = $8
2. A. 5 x 3 =   15 lollipops
3. A. 7 x 8 =   56 balloon animals
4. B. 9 x 4 =   36 folders
5. B. 4 x 5 =   20 jobs

Pages 67–69

1. D. 94 x 2 =   188 paddles
2. A. 68 x 12 =   816 books
3. B. 49 x 6 =   294 pretzels
4. B. 48 x 24 =   1,152 cans of lemonade
5. C. $115 x 3 = $345

Pages 70–72

1. B. 64 ÷ 8 =   8 pencils
2. C. $288 ÷ 2 = $144
3. D. 84 ÷ 14 =   6 rocks
4. A. 348 ÷ 6 =   58 sandwiches
5. C. 50 ÷ 6 =   8 groups of balloons/2 balloons for the mailbox (8 R2)

Pages 73–75

1. C. 345 + 67 =   then   412 + 78 =   490 stickers
2. A. $28 ÷ 2 =   then $14 x 4 = $56
3. B. 624 ÷ 6 =   then   104 x 8 =   832
4. D. 3,456 – 144 =   then   3,312 + 289 = 3,601 people
5. B. 34 – 18 =   then   16 x 6 =   96 pictures